ELEMENTARY LEVEL

Series Editor: John Milne

The Heinemann ELT Guided Readers provide a choice of enjoyable reading material for learners of English. The series is published at five levels – Starter, Beginner, Elementary, Intermediate and Upper. At **Elementary Level**, the control of content and language has the following main features:

Information Control

Stories have straightforward plots and a restricted number of main characters. Information which is vital to the understanding of the story is clearly presented and repeated when necessary. Difficult allusion and metaphor are avoided and cultural backgrounds are made explicit.

Structure Control

Students will meet those grammatical features which they have already been taught in their elementary course of studies. Other grammatical features occasionally occur with which the students may not be so familiar, but their use is made clear through context and reinforcement. This ensures that the reading as well as being enjoyable provides a continual learning situation for the students. Sentences are kept short – a maximum of two clauses in nearly all cases – and within sentences there is a balanced use of simple adverbial and adjectival phrases. Great care is taken with pronoun reference.

Vocabulary Control

At **Elementary Level** there is a limited use of a carefully controlled vocabulary of approximately 1,100 basic words. At the same time, students are given some opportunity to meet new or unfamiliar words in contexts where their meaning is obvious. The meaning of words introduced in this way is reinforced by repetition. Help is also given to the students in the form of vivid illustrations which are closely related to the text.

Contents

A Note About the Author

William Somerset Maugham is one of the most famous British writers.

Maugham was born in Paris in 1874. He studied medicine to become a doctor. His first book, called *Lisa of Lambeth*, was published in 1896. It was successful and many copies were sold.

Maugham decided not to work as a doctor, but to be a writer instead. He wrote a great number of books and plays. And many of his stories were about the people he met on his travels all over the world.

Maugham became a rich man. 80 million copies of his books were sold while he was alive.

Somerset Maugham died in Cap Ferrat, France, on 16th December 1965. He was 91 years old.

THE
ESCAPE

THE ESCAPE

Roger Charing is a friend of mine. One day, he told me he was going to get married. I was very surprised when he told me. Let me tell you why I was surprised.

Roger was about forty years old. He was tall and handsome. And he was very rich. Many women wanted to marry him. But he had always escaped. He was forty years old, but he was not married.

I have another friend, also handsome and rich. A woman wanted to marry him. He tried to escape. He got on a boat and sailed round the world. He was away for a year. When he got back, the woman was waiting for him. She was waiting for him on the dockside as the boat came into the harbour.

But Roger Charing always escaped. He did not want a wife. He was happy to live the life of an unmarried man. He wanted to be a bachelor. But then he met Ruth Barlow.

Ruth was younger than Roger. She was quite good-looking and she had big, beautiful, dark eyes. Men always felt sorry for Ruth. She looked at them with her big, dark eyes, which often had tears in them. When a man saw those big, sad eyes, he wanted to help her.

Roger met Ruth at a party. When he saw those big, dark eyes, he fell in love with her. He immediately wanted to look after her and make her happy.

I had known Ruth for some years and I did not like her. She used her eyes to make men feel sorry for her. She had been married twice and both her husbands were dead. Now she was a widow and lived alone in a small house in London. I was sure she was looking for another husband.

*Roger met Ruth at a party. When he saw those big, dark eyes,
he fell in love with her.*

Roger told me he was going to marry her.

'Ruth has had a very sad life he said. 'She has married two husbands and they are both dead. I want to marry her and make her happy.'

'I hope you will be happy,' I replied. But I did not think he would be happy. I thought he was making a mistake.

Roger got engaged to Ruth. He put a notice in the newspapers so that all his friends knew about the engagement. Roger bought Ruth a beautiful engagement ring. It was very expensive. He took her out to the theatre. They dined together in expensive restaurants. He seemed very happy.

Then, suddenly, something happened between Roger and Ruth. Roger never told me what had happened. But I think I know. Roger did not love Ruth any more. He did not want to marry her.

But Roger had a problem. He had become engaged to Ruth. He had promised to marry her. If he broke his promise, Ruth would take him to court. Roger was a very rich man. The court would make Roger pay Ruth a lot of money. This was the law at that time. This was his problem.

Roger knew that Ruth was clever. She had made him promise to marry her. But Roger was clever too. He planned his escape.

Roger did not tell Ruth that he no longer loved her. He took her out to the theatre. They ate in expensive restaurants. He gave her expensive presents.

'When are we going to get married?' Ruth asked him one day.

'When we find a nice house to live in,' Roger replied. 'We'll get married when we find the right house.'

'That's very kind of you,' said Ruth. 'But please let us get married soon. I love you.'

'Tomorrow I'll get a list of houses for sale,' Roger said to Ruth. 'We'll go and look at them together. When we see the perfect house, we'll buy it. And then we'll get married.'

Roger got a long list of houses for sale. Then he and Ruth went to look at the houses. But there was something wrong with every house on the list. Roger found something wrong with each one.

'This is a nice house,' said Ruth.

'Yes, it is,' replied Roger. 'It's very nice. But it's very dark. The windows are too small. It's not good enough for you. You will not be happy here.'

Then they went and looked at another house.

'This one is very beautiful,' said Ruth.

'Yes, it is,' agreed Roger. 'It's very beautiful. But it's too small.'

They looked at many, many houses. But Roger found something wrong with each one. Sometimes the house was too large. Sometimes the house was too small. Sometimes the house was too noisy. Sometimes the house was too quiet. There was something wrong with every house they saw.

'We must find a house soon,' said Ruth unhappily. 'I'm getting tired of looking at houses.'

'We'll find one soon,' said Roger. 'Soon we'll find the perfect house. When we find the right house, we'll buy it. Then we'll get married.'

Roger got more and more lists of houses. Every day he took Ruth with him. They looked at more and more houses. And he found something wrong with all of them.

After five weeks, Ruth got tired of looking at houses. She felt tired and unhappy. Roger and Ruth went up the stairs and then down the stairs in every house. Up and down and round and round, day after day, week after week.

'We'll never get married,' Ruth said one day, unhappily. 'We won't get married for years and years.'

'Don't be unhappy,' said Roger. 'We'll find the right house soon. I'm sure of it. I've just had a list of another sixty houses. I'm sure one of them will be suitable.'

One day, after looking at three more houses, Ruth lost her temper. She was very angry.

'We must find a house soon,' she said to Roger. 'If we don't find a house soon, I may not marry you. Perhaps, I'll marry another man.'

'Be patient,' said Roger quietly. 'Don't be angry with me. We'll go and look at more houses tomorrow. I'm sure we'll find the right one tomorrow.'

So off they went again, looking at more and more houses. Roger was happy. His plan was working.

Then, one day, they looked at five houses, one after the other. In the evening, Ruth was tired and angry. Roger showed her another list of houses for sale. Ruth lost her temper completely.

'Do you want to marry me or not?' she shouted at Roger.

'Of course I want to marry you,' replied Roger quietly. 'We'll get married as soon as we find the right house. There's another twenty houses on this list. I'm sure one of them will be the right house for us. We'll go and look at them tomorrow.'

The next morning, Ruth did not feel well.

'I'm tired of looking at houses,' she told Roger. 'I don't want to look at another house. I never want to see another house in my life.'

'I'm sorry you don't feel well,' said Roger. 'You stay at home and rest. I'll go and look at the houses. I'm sure I'll find the right one.'

13

Roger showed her another list of houses for sale.

The next day, Roger received a letter from Ruth.

Roger,
I do not believe you really love me. I have found another man.
He loves me and wants to take care of me. I am going to marry
him today. Ruth

Roger immediately sent her a reply.

Ruth,
Your letter has made me very unhappy. I am very miserable. But
I wish you and your husband happiness. I am sending with this
letter a list of another seven houses. Perhaps one of them will be
the right one for you. Roger

So Roger did not get married to Ruth. And he had not
broken his promise. So he did not have to pay her any
money. She had changed her mind.

Today, Roger is a bachelor. He is a rich man. He has
escaped!

LOUISE

LOUISE

I met Louise twenty-five years ago. She was a young and attractive woman. We have been friends since then. But it has been a strange friendship.

She did not like me. I was sure of that. She never told me that she did not like me. But other friends have told me. She has often said unkind things about me to them. And these friends have told me what Louise has said.

When I was with her, she always pretended to like me. But why did she pretend? Why did she want me to be her friend?

Louise told everybody that she had a weak heart. And they believed her. Everyone believed what she told them. But I did not. I did not believe that she had a weak heart. Was that why she pretended to like me? Did she want to show me that I was wrong?

When Louise was a young girl, she had a bad illness. When she grew older, her parents did not want her to get married. They did not think she was strong enough. They wanted her to stay at home. They wanted to look after her.

Then she met Tom Maitland. Tom was a handsome man. He was big and strong – and he was very rich.

'Will you marry me?' Tom asked her one day.

'Yes, I'll marry you,' she replied. 'But you know I am not very strong. I have a weak heart. We will have to live quietly if you marry me.'

'I'll look after you,' said Tom.

'Thank you,' said Louise. 'I won't live for many years. So I won't trouble you for very long.'

19

'I'll do everything I can to make you happy,' said Tom. 'I love you very much.'

So they got married. Tom stayed at home to look after Louise. He often wanted to go out and play golf with his friends. But he never did.

Louise told him to go out. They often had an argument.

'You must go out and play golf with your friends,' Louise said. 'I want you to enjoy yourself.'

Finally, Tom agreed to go out. But when he got to the door of the house, Louise had a heart attack. She had to go to bed. Tom did not go out. He stayed at home to look after her.

After a year, Louise had a daughter. They called her Iris. They both loved Iris very much and they seemed happy.

I often met Louise and Tom at dinners or at parties. I noticed something interesting about Louise. If it was an amusing party, Louise was able to stay until late at night. But if it was a dull party, she felt unwell. And Tom had to take her home.

Once I was at a party which was very enjoyable. Louise stayed at the party until five in the morning.

'You are enjoying yourself,' I said to her.

'I am staying here to please Tom,' she replied.

'You are strong enough to do the things you like,' I told her.

'Do you want me to drop down dead? That would please you,' was her angry reply.

But it was Tom who died. One day, they were out in a boat on the river. It was very cold and Tom gave his overcoat to Louise. It started to rain and he got very wet. He caught a bad cold and died a few days later.

Tom left Louise a lot of money. Louise was very sad at the

When he got to the door of the house, Louise had a heart attack.

death of her husband. Her friends were very sorry for Louise. And they were sorry for her young daughter, Iris.

Her friends did everything to help Louise. She did not have to do anything herself. They looked after her and they looked after Iris.

'I don't know what I am going to do,' she said. 'I am not strong. I may die any day. How can I look after my little daughter? I need someone to look after me.'

'Why don't you marry again?' her friends asked her.

'I am not strong enough,' she replied. 'No one wants to marry a sick woman.'

I don't know why, but many young men wanted to marry her. A year after Tom's death, Louise married her second husband. His name was George Hobhouse.

'I am not strong,' Louise told George. 'I won't live for many years. I won't trouble you for very long.'

George Hobhouse was an officer in the army. He liked being an officer in the army. He wanted to stay in the army and succeed.

Unfortunately, Louise had a heart attack. She had to go and live in the South of France. The weather in England was too cold for her. So George had to leave the army. He had to go with Louise to look after her and Iris.

For the next two or three years, George lived with Louise in the South of France. Louise was well enough to go out to dinners and parties every evening. She often stayed at a party which went on until very late at night. But she was not well enough to go back and live in England.

George Hobhouse did not like living in the South of France. He had nothing to do all day. He wanted to go back to England, but he could not. He had to look after his wife who had a weak heart.

Then the war broke out. George had to go back into the army. Three months later, he was killed in a battle.

Louise did not have a heart attack when she heard of George's death. Instead, she became very busy. She turned her large house in the South of France into a hospital. Her house became a hospital for wounded officers. Other people did all the work, of course.

Louise had to be careful because of her weak heart. But she was able to go out to dinners and parties. She went out with the young officers when they got better.

I met her once in an expensive restaurant in Paris. She was with a tall and very handsome young Frenchman.

'I'm here on business,' she told me. 'I'm doing hospital work. I'm not feeling well. But I have to do as much as I can.'

'You don't look ill,' I told her. 'You look very well and very happy.'

She did not like the way I spoke to her.

'Why do you never believe me?' she asked, with anger in her voice. 'I went to a doctor this morning. He told me my heart is very weak. I have not long to live.'

'You have lived for twenty years with your weak heart,' I replied. 'Perhaps you will live for another twenty years.'

When the war came to an end, Louise came back to live in London. She was now over forty. But she still looked young. She did not look more than twenty-five. She had always found someone to look after her.

Iris had been at school during the war. She was now grown up. She came to live with Louise. Iris was a good girl. She stayed at home to look after her mother.

'Don't you think Iris should go out more?' I once asked Louise. 'Why doesn't she go out with young people?'

23

'I often tell her that,' was Louise's reply. 'But she won't listen to me.'

Later, I found out the truth.

'You must go out with your friends and enjoy yourself,' Louise often said to Iris. 'I want you to go out.'

But when Iris agreed to go out, Louise had a heart attack. She had to go to bed. Iris had to stay at home and look after her.

Then Iris met a young man and fell in love with him. He asked her to marry him. But Iris told him she had to stay at home. She had to look after her mother.

The young man was a friend of mine. He came to see me. He was very unhappy and asked me to help him. I liked the young man and decided to help him. I went to see Louise.

'It's not my fault,' Louise told me. 'I have asked Iris to leave me. I have told her to marry this young man. But she won't. She says she must stay at home and look after me.'

'Isn't it sad for the young man and for Iris?' I said.

'Of course, it is,' replied Louise. 'But it won't be for very long. My heart is much worse. I won't last more than another month or two.'

'My dear Louise, you have buried two husbands. I don't see why you should not bury two more.'

Louise became very angry.

'I know what you think,' she said. 'You think that I am not ill at all.'

I looked at her for a few seconds.

'That's right,' I said. 'I have never believed you. You are always able to do what you want. You are ill when you want to be ill. You are cruel and selfish.'

I thought Louise would become very angry. But she didn't. She smiled.

24

As she was dying, she spoke her last words to her daughter.

'My friend,' she said, 'one day you will be sorry you said those cruel words.'

'Are you going to let Iris marry this young man?' I asked her.

'Iris can marry the young man if she wants.'

'Have you told her that?' I asked her.

'Yes, I have. Many times.'

'And have you told Iris that her marriage will kill you?'

'Yes, I have. I know I have not long to live.'

'You always say that,' I told her. 'I'm sure you will live for many more years.'

'Don't you feel sorry for me?'

'I feel more sorry for Iris,' I replied.

'Very well,' she said. 'She can marry the young man. If it kills me, it kills me.'

And so it was arranged. The wedding date was fixed. A beautiful wedding dress was made for Iris. Invitations were sent out. Iris and the young man both looked very happy.

At ten o'clock on the morning of the wedding, Louise had a heart attack. She was carried to her bed and died a few moments later.

She was a cruel and selfish woman. As she was dying, she spoke her last words to her daughter.

'I knew I would die on your wedding-day,' she said. 'But I forgive you.'

THE ANT
AND THE
GRASSHOPPER

THE ANT AND THE GRASSHOPPER

Have you heard the story of The Ant and The Grasshopper? I had to learn it at school when I was a boy.

It is a simple story. It is meant to teach young children a lesson. The lesson is that you must work hard in life. Those who work hard will be successful. Those who do not work hard will do badly.

In the story, the ant works hard all summer. Every day, the ant goes out and collects food. By the end of the summer, the ant is ready for winter. It has a large store of food. But the grasshopper does no work. It sits in the sun and sings all day.

Then the winter comes. The grasshopper has no food. It goes to the ant and asks for something to eat.

'What did you do all summer?' asks the ant.

'I sang,' replies the grasshopper. 'I sat in the sun and sang all day.'

'Now you can go and dance,' says the ant.

I did not like this story. It did not make me want to work harder. It made me think that ants were cruel. The story made me hate ants. Whenever I saw an ant, I used to stamp on it with my foot.

'That will teach you to be cruel to the grasshopper,' I said.

A few days ago, I remembered this story of the ant and the grasshopper. I went into a restaurant to have lunch. I saw a friend, George Ramsay. George was sitting at a table alone. He looked very miserable.

'Hello, George,' I said. 'How are you?'

'I don't feel well,' he replied.

'What's wrong?' I asked, sitting down at the table. 'Is it your brother Tom? Has he got into trouble again?'

'Yes,' he replied. 'It's Tom.'

Let me tell you about Tom. In every respectable family, there is one person who does badly. In George's family, this person was his brother, Tom.

At first, Tom was successful. He had gone into business. He had married and had two children. Then one day, he said that he did not like work. He wanted to enjoy himself.

He left his wife and his office. He went to Europe. He had a little money. He spent it freely. He stayed at the best hotels. He dined in the most expensive restaurants. He went to parties with beautiful women. He enjoyed himself.

His family heard stories about him. They shook their heads sadly.

'What will he do when his money is finished?' they asked each other.

They soon found out the answer to this question. Tom was well-liked. He was amusing and had many friends. When his money was finished, Tom borrowed money from his friends.

He did not borrow large amounts of money. So his friends did not ask him to give it back. I often met him. I liked him and found him amusing. But each time I met him, he borrowed some money.

Tom borrowed small amounts of money from his friends. When he needed larger sums of money, he borrowed them from his brother, George.

George was very respectable. He worked hard and was careful with money. He wanted his brother to become respectable. Tom promised George that he would change. If George lent him enough money, Tom promised to make a new start. He would go back into business and work hard.

Once, Tom bought an expensive motor car with George's money. The next time, he used the money to live in an expensive hotel in Paris.

George became tired of Tom's promises. He refused to give Tom any more money. Then something terrible happened. Tom almost went to prison. George was terribly upset. It would be shameful for him and for his family if Tom was sent to prison.

Tom had tricked a man called Cronshaw. He had cheated Cronshaw out of a large sum of money. Cronshaw was going to take Tom to court. Tom was going to go to prison if Cronshaw did not get his money back. George had to pay Cronshaw five hundred pounds.

As soon as George paid the money, Cronshaw and Tom left for Monte Carlo. They were seen together in Monte Carlo. They had a happy time there spending George's money. George was furious. I have never seen George so angry.

For twenty years Tom lived a happy life. For twenty years he stayed at the best hotels and ate in the best restaurants. For twenty years he enjoyed the company of beautiful women. Although he was forty-six, he looked much younger. He had lots of friends.

George worked hard all his life. He went to his office at half past nine every morning. He never left before six in the evening. He saved his money and looked after his family. He had no time to enjoy himself. George was only forty-seven. But he looked sixty.

George was glad that he was growing old.

George was very respectable . . .

. . . Tom lived a happy life.

'Tom is growing older too,' he once told me. 'When he was young and handsome it was easy for him to make friends.

'Tom will be fifty in four years' time. What will he do then? I will have saved thirty thousand pounds when I am fifty. Tom will have nothing. We will see which is best – to work hard or to play all the time.'

I sat at the table and looked at George. Poor George. I felt sorry for him.

'What has happened this time?' I asked him.

I wondered what Tom had done wrong. Had he been arrested by the police? Was he really going to prison this time?

'I have worked hard all my life,' said George.

'That's true,' I said.

'And you know that Tom has not done any work for the last twenty years. He should spend the rest of his life in poverty and misery.'

I had to agree.

George's face grew red with anger. He was so angry that he found it difficult to speak.

'A few weeks ago, Tom became engaged to an old woman,' he said at last. 'The woman was old enough to be his mother. Now she has died. And she has left him everything she had. She's left him half a million pounds and a large house in London and a large house in the country.'

George beat his fist down on the table. He was in a rage.

I was not able to stop myself. I laughed out loud. It was the funniest story I had heard for a long time. The grasshopper had done better than the ant.

George never forgave me for my laughter. He never spoke to me again. But Tom often asks me to dinner in his large house in the most expensive part of London.

But he has not changed. As I am leaving, he often asks me to lend him a pound.

THE FALL
OF
EDWARD
BARNARD

THE FALL OF
EDWARD BARNARD

Bateman Hunter and Edward Barnard were friends for many years. They went to college together. That is where they met Isabel Longstaffe.

Bateman and Edward met Isabel at a tea party. And they both fell in love with her. But Bateman thought that Isabel was in love with Edward.

Bateman was sad that Isabel had chosen Edward. Bateman wanted Isabel to marry him. But Bateman did not tell Isabel about his love for her. He stayed friends with Edward and with Isabel.

Six months later, Isabel and Edward were engaged to be married. There were parties and dances. Bateman was always there. Isabel was going to be married to his best friend, but he did not stop loving her.

Then something terrible happened. Edward Barnard, father had all his money in a bank. The bank used its money unwisely and had to close. Edward Barnard's father lost all his money. He came home one night. He told his wife that he was penniless. Then, after dinner, he went into his library and shot himself.

A week later, Edward Barnard went to see Isabel. He looked tired and miserable.

'Isabel,' he said sadly, 'I am penniless. I cannot marry you now.'

'But you must marry me,' said Isabel. 'I love you. I want you to marry me.'

39

'But your father will not allow you to marry me,' said Edward. 'I haven't any money at all.'

'I don't care,' was Isabel's reply. 'I love you.'

Then Edward told her his plans. George Braunschmidt, an old friend of his family, had offered him a job. The job was in one of Braunschmidt's company offices. The office was in the South Pacific. Edward had to leave for Tahiti immediately.

'I have to work in the office in Tahiti for two years,' Edward told Isabel. 'When I have learnt the business, I will come back here to Chicago. I will have a job here in Braunschmidt's head office.

'Are you ready to wait for me?' asked Edward. 'You will have to wait for two years.'

'Of course I shall wait for you,' replied Isabel. 'I love you. I will wait for you. When you come back, I will marry you.'

The evening before he left for Tahiti, Edward had dinner with Isabel and her family. After dinner, Mr Longstaffe told Edward he wanted to talk to him privately. They went to his library together.

'Have you ever heard of Arnold Jackson?' Mr Longstaffe asked Edward.

In every family, there is one person who behaves badly. In most families, there is one person who has got into trouble and done something shameful. In Mrs Longstaffe's family, that person was Arnold Jackson.

Arnold Jackson was Mrs Longstaffe's brother. He had been a rich banker. He was respected by everyone. Everyone thought he was an honest man. Then something terrible happened. Arnold Jackson was arrested by the police.

Arnold Jackson had been stealing from his bank for many years. Arnold Jackson was a thief. He was sent to prison for seven years. After he came out of prison, Arnold Jackson left America. He went to live in Tahiti.

'Yes, I have heard of Arnold Jackson,' Edward said to Mr Longstaffe.

'Everyone in Chicago has heard of Arnold Jackson,' said Mr Longstaffe sadly. 'Arnold Jackson is Mrs Longstaffe's brother. We have not heard from him for many years. We know he is living in Tahiti. I advise you to keep away from him. But, if you do hear anything about him, please let us know. Mrs Longstaffe and I would be glad to know how he is.'

'Of course,' replied Edward.

'That's all I wanted to say to you. Let's go back to Isabel and her mother.'

Isabel was sad that Edward had to leave. But she was proud of him. Edward was going out to Tahiti to be successful in business. Soon he would return to Chicago. When he came back, he would have a job and some money. Then they would be able to get married.

Two years passed. Edward wrote a letter to Isabel every month. She received twenty-four letters from him. Isabel liked to read Edward's letters. They were interesting and amusing.

But, at the end of the second year, something strange happened. Edward did not say anything in his letters about coming back. Isabel became worried. She read all the letters again. Then she noticed something strange about them. The later letters were more amusing than the earlier letters. Edward seemed happier in Tahiti than he had been in Chicago.

Isabel began to worry about Edward. She spoke to Bateman Hunter about her worries.

41

'Edward has changed,' she said to Bateman. 'He is not the same as he was two years ago,

Isabel read out all Edward's letters.

'Don't you think there is something strange about these last letters?' she said. 'He doesn't write about returning to Chicago.'

Bateman noticed that Isabel was really worried. He still loved her, of course. And he was ready to do anything to help her.

Bateman met Isabel a few days later. Isabel noticed immediately that Bateman was worried.

'What's wrong?' she asked. 'Have you heard from Edward? Has something happened?'

Bateman did not know how to answer Isabel's questions. He did not want to make her unhappy. But he saw that she wanted an answer.

'I asked Mr Braunschmidt about Edward,' he told Isabel. 'Mr Braunschmidt told me that Edward had left his company in Tahiti nearly a year ago.'

'How strange!' said Isabel. 'Why didn't Edward say anything about it in his letters?'

Bateman did not want to upset Isabel. He did not want to tell her the rest of his news. But he had to tell her everything.

'Edward didn't leave Braunschmidt's company,' he went on. 'He was dismissed. Mr Braunschmidt said that Edward was fired. He was ordered to leave because he was lazy and did not do his job properly.'

'How terrible!' said Isabel.

Bateman saw that she was crying. Bateman held her hand. Isabel was so upset that she did not take her hand away.

'Don't cry,' Bateman said to Isabel. 'I have a plan.'

Bateman worked in his father's company, the Hunter Automobile Company. The company had an office in the South Pacific.

'My father has agreed that I can visit our office there,' Bateman told Isabel. 'On my way back, I can stay for a few days in Tahiti. I will meet Edward and find out what has happened.'

'You're wonderful!' Isabel said to Bateman. 'What a kind man you are!'

Isabel looked at Bateman. He was still holding her hand. He looked into her eyes.

'I will do everything I can to make you happy,' he said. 'I will go to Tahiti and find Edward. And I will do my best to bring him back here to Chicago.'

———

Bateman arrived in Tahiti a few weeks later. A young man carried his bags to a hotel. On the way to the hotel, Bateman spoke to the young man.

'I'm looking for Mr Edward Barnard,' he said. 'Do you know him?'

The young man was not sure who Edward Barnard was.

'He's an American,' said Bateman. 'He is tall and has light brown hair and blue eyes. He's been here in Tahiti for more than two years.'

'You mean Mr Jackson's nephew,' said the young man.

'I think that is a different person,' said Bateman coldly.

Bateman was amazed when he heard Arnold Jackson's name. Why hadn't Jackson changed his name? Everyone knew that he had been to prison. And who was this nephew? Isabel was the only child of Mr and Mrs Longstaffe. Jackson had a niece, but he did not have a nephew.

Bateman left his bags in the hotel and went to the offices of Braunschmidt. He asked the manager where Edward Barnard now worked. The manager told him that Edward Barnard worked in a shop called Cameron's.

Bateman went to Cameron's. It was a small shop. Edward was behind the counter selling cloth to a young woman. Bateman was amazed. Why was Edward selling cloth in a small shop?

When Edward saw Bateman, he gave a cry of joy.

'Bateman,' he said. 'How wonderful to see you! Sit down and we'll have a long talk.'

'But we can't talk here,' said Bateman.come along to my hotel. We can talk there in private. Can you leave your work?'

'Of course I can leave my work,' replied Edward. 'This is Tahiti. We don't work here as you do in Chicago.'

They walked together to the hotel. Edward began the conversation.

'You know that I was fired from Braunschmidt's?' he asked.

Bateman was amazed. It was shameful to be fired. But Edward did not feel any shame at all.

'You won't become rich in a small shop selling cloth,' Bateman said coldly.

'That's true,' agreed Edward, with a smile. 'But I make enough money for what I need. That's all I want.'

'You did not think this way two years ago,' said Bateman.

'I am now wiser,' said Edward, again with a smile.

Bateman looked at the man walking beside him. Edward was dressed in white trousers, which were not very clean. And he had a large straw hat on his head, like the hats worn by the Tahitians. His face was browned by the sun and he looked very healthy. He had a happy smile on his face all the time. This smile puzzled Bateman.

I can't understand it, Bateman thought to himself. Why is he so happy? He has lost a good job and is working in a small shop selling cloth. He has no reason to be happy.

They arrived at the hotel and sat down on the terrace. From the terrace, they looked down on the street below. Edward asked Bateman many questions about Chicago. But Edward's questions puzzled Bateman.

Edward asked questions about friends, about Bateman's father, about many different people and places. Edward also asked about Isabel. But he did not ask any special question about Isabel. Had he forgotten that he was going to be married to Isabel?

As Bateman was thinking about this, an older man came up to their table. He was a tall, thin man with curly white hair. He was wearing white trousers. He looked happy and healthy.

'This is my friend, Bateman Hunter,' said Edward, introducing Bateman to the man.

The man took Bateman's hand in a strong, friendly hold. Then Edward told Bateman the man's name.

'This is Mr Arnold Jackson,' said Edward.

Bateman's face went white and his hands went cold. This was the man who had been sent to prison for seven years. Bateman did not know what to say. Arnold Jackson looked at Bateman and smiled.

'I'm sure you have heard my name before,' he said.

Bateman did not know what to say. Arnold and Edward were both smiling. They both seemed to be amused.

'Edward has told me about you,' went on Arnold Jackson. 'I understand you are a friend of the Longstaffes. Mary Longstaffe is my sister.'

Bateman was becoming more and more uncomfortable. Arnold Jackson did not seem ashamed. He spoke about his family in Chicago as if nothing had happened.

'I can't stay to talk to you now,' said Arnold Jackson. 'I'm busy. You must both come and have a meal with me tonight.'

'That's very kind of you, Mr Jackson,' said Bateman coldly. 'But I am only here for a short time. My boat leaves

46

tomorrow. I am unable to accept your invitation.'

'Of course you can come,' said Arnold Jackson. 'My wife is an excellent cook. You can have a very good dinner. And you can tell me all about Chicago and about my sister. Edward will show you the way to my house. I'll see you tonight.'

And before Bateman was able to say anything more, Arnold Jackson had gone.

Bateman sat silently for some time. Then he turned to Edward.

'What does he mean?' he asked. 'His wife is in Chicago.'

'He must be talking about another wife,' said Edward with a smile.

'What a terrible man!' said Bateman. 'Do you see him often?'

'Yes, I do. He tells everyone that I am his nephew.'

'But how can you be friends with him? He has been in prison. He's a criminal.'

'Perhaps he is a criminal,' replied Edward. 'But he's an interesting person. He's taught me everything I know.'

'What has he taught you?' asked Bateman in amazement.

'He has taught me how to live a happy life.'

'He's a fine teacher!' said Bateman. 'Did he teach you to work in a small shop selling cheap cloth?'

'Come with me tonight,' said Edward. 'I'm sure you will have an enjoyable evening.'

Bateman was about to say no. But Edward went on talking.

'We have been friends for many years, Bateman. Please do not refuse.'

'Because I am your friend, I will come,' said Bateman.

'Now I must get back to work,' said Edward. I'll meet

you here at the hotel at five. We'll go to Arnold's house together.'

'Aren't you staying in this hotel?' asked Bateman. 'I believe it's the best hotel in Tahiti.'

'Stay here in this hotel? Not me. It's far too expensive. I have a small room outside the town. It's cheap and clean.'

'When you lived in Chicago, you always wanted the best things.'

'Chicago,' said Edward, with a strange smile.

'Chicago is the greatest city in the world,' said Bateman. 'I hope you have not forgotten that.'

'No, I haven't forgotten.'

'When are you coming back?' asked Bateman.

'I often wonder,' said Edward, again with that strange smile on his face.

Bateman was once more amazed. He wanted Edward to explain. But Edward hurried off down the steps.

———

Arnold Jackson's house was on a hill looking over the sea. They were met by a tall, handsome Tahitian woman.

'This is my friend Bateman Hunter,' said Edward. 'We're going to have dinner with you tonight, Lavina.'

The woman nodded and went into the house.

'Who's that?' asked Bateman.

'That's Arnold's wife, Lavina.'

Bateman said nothing.

Lavina came back with Arnold Jackson.

Arnold Jackson led them back to the house.

'Look behind you,' he said to the two young men.

They stood on the steps and looked out over the Pacific

Ocean. The water was a beautiful silver colour in the evening light.

'Isn't that beautiful?' said Arnold Jackson.

Bateman had to agree. It was a beautiful sight.

A young woman came and sat with them at the dinner table.

'Mr Hunter, this is my daughter, Eva,' said Arnold Jackson to Bateman.

Eva was beautiful. She had red lips and her skin was brown. Her long, black hair hung down over her shoulders.

At dinner, they talked about Chicago. Arnold Jackson wanted to hear all the news. The food was excellent and Bateman began to enjoy himself. Then Arnold Jackson spoke about the time when he was in prison.

Bateman's face turned red.

What a strange man, he thought to himself. He talks about prison as if it was a hotel.

After dinner, they sat outside and talked. Arnold Jackson talked about the many strange and interesting people he had met. He talked about the strange lives they lived. Bateman became interested.

But then he remembered Chicago. What would people think? He was having dinner with Arnold Jackson. Everyone in Chicago knew he was a criminal. What would Mr Longstaffe think? What would Isabel think?

At last, Bateman said it was time for him to leave. He wanted to go back to his hotel.

'The road is not safe in the dark,' said Edward. 'Stay here for the night. You can get up early. I'll take you back to your hotel in the morning.'

Bateman agreed to stay. Before going to bed, Bateman and Edward talked together.

After dinner, they sat outside and talked.

'Edward, when are you coming back to Chicago?' asked Bateman.

'I don't know. Perhaps I will never go back to Chicago.'

'What do you mean?' cried Bateman.

'I am happy here,' replied Edward. 'Why should I leave?'

'But you must not stay here,' said Bateman. 'You cannot stay here working in a small shop. Please come back to Chicago.'

'But I am happy here,' replied Edward quietly. 'Why should I leave a place where I am happy?'

'But what about your life in Chicago?' asked Bateman. 'What about your family and your friends? What about making money?'

'I am not so sure that making money is important,' said Edward.

'Is that a lesson Arnold Jackson has taught you?'

'I have learnt many things from him,' replied Edward quietly. 'There are more important things in life than making money. Perhaps it is more important to be happy.'

'But what about Isabel's happiness?' asked Bateman. 'Isn't that important? Tell me. Are you going to marry Isabel?'

'I promised to marry her. And I will if she wants me. But I am not good enough for her. I will never be rich. You must tell her that, Bateman.'

'Me? Tell her what you have just said? I cannot! It will make her terribly unhappy. She loves you. How can I give her such a message?'

'Why don't you marry her, Bateman? You have been in love with her since we were at college. You will both be very happy.'

'Stop!' said Bateman angrily. 'I don't want to listen. If

Isabel hears about this, she will not want to marry you. What will you do then?'

'I will marry Arnold's daughter, Eva,' replied Edward immediately.

Bateman looked at Edward. Edward was not smiling. Edward was speaking the truth.

'Tell Isabel what I have told you,' said Edward. 'I'm sure she will understand.'

———

Two weeks later, Bateman arrived back in Chicago. He was very glad to be back. He phoned Isabel as soon as he got home.

'You must have lots to tell me,' said Isabel on the phone. 'Come and have dinner with us tonight.'

Bateman was surprised. Isabel had been waiting a long time for news of Edward. Why hadn't she asked about Edward when they were speaking on the phone?

Bateman had a pleasant dinner with Isabel and her father and mother. They did not talk about Tahiti. They talked about what was happening in Chicago.

At last dinner was over. As they were leaving the dining–room, Isabel took Bateman by the hand.

'Bateman and I are going to the library,' she said to her mother and father. 'We have a lot to talk about.'

They sat down in the comfortable chairs in the library.

'Now tell me your news,' said Isabel.

'I don't know where to begin,' said Bateman. 'I don't know what to say.'

'Is Edward Barnard coming back?'

'No.'

There was a long silence before Bateman was able to go on. Then he told her the whole story. At the end, Isabel asked only one question. And it surprised Bateman.

'What's Uncle Arnold's daughter like? Does she look like me?'

'I don't know,' replied Bateman. 'I didn't look at her carefully.'

'Was she pretty?'

'Yes, she was pretty.'

'It doesn't matter,' said Isabel. 'We don't need to think about her any more.'

'What are you going to do, Isabel?' asked Bateman.

Isabel looked down at the ring on her left hand. She was wearing the engagement ring that Edward had given her.

'I stayed engaged to Edward because I wanted to help him,' she said. 'I thought he would work hard in Tahiti if we were engaged. But it is no good. Edward has failed.'

She took the ring off her finger. She put it down on the table. Bateman's heart began to beat quickly.

'You're wonderful,' he said. 'You stayed engaged to Edward to help him. You were not thinking of your own happiness.'

She smiled and stood up.

'Thank you for your help, Bateman,' she said. 'I knew I could trust you. And I was right.'

He took her hand and held it. She looked very beautiful.

'Isabel, I will do anything to make you happy,' he said. 'Isabel, I love you.'

He took her into his arms and held her tightly.

'I loved you from the first moment I met you,' he said. 'I wanted to ask you to marry me when we first met.'

He took her hand and held it. She looked very beautiful.

'Then why didn't you ask me?' she asked. 'I have loved you too.'

She loved him! He could not believe what she was saying. She had always loved him!

As he held her in his arms, he had a dream. Bateman dreamt that the Hunter Automobile Company was growing bigger and bigger. He dreamt that he was growing richer and richer. He dreamt that he was living with Isabel in a beautiful house. He dreamt of dinner-parties with wonderful people.

Isabel stayed quietly in Bateman's arms.

'Poor Edward,' she said.

POINTS
FOR
UNDERSTANDING

Points for Understanding

THE ESCAPE

1 What happened when Roger met Ruth?
2 Maugham, the writer of these stories, did not like Ruth Barlow.
  (a) Why did men feel sorry for Ruth?
  (b) What did Maugham think she was looking for?
3 Something happened between Roger and Ruth. What did Maugham think had happened?
4 What was Roger's problem?
5 'When are we going to get married?' Ruth asked Roger. What was Roger's reply?
6 Roger and Ruth went to look at houses for sale. What happened each time they looked at a house?
7 Roger had planned his escape from Ruth.
  (a) How did Roger escape from marrying Ruth?
  (b) How did he escape from paying her any money?

LOUISE

1 How did Maugham know Louise did not like him?
2 What did Louise tell everyone?
3 Did Maugham believe Louise?
4 Why did Louise's parents not want her to get married?
5 Describe Tom Maitland.
6 'You must go out and play golf with your friends,' Louise said. What happened when Tom Maitland agreed to go out?
7 Maugham noticed something interesting about Louise. What did he notice?
8 What happened to Tom Maitland?
9 Louise married George Hobhouse.
  (a) What was George Hobhouse's job?
  (b) Did he like his job?
  (c) Why did he have to leave his job?
10 What happened to George Hobhouse?

11 Maugham met Louise once in an expensive restaurant in Paris.
    (a)   Did he think Louise looked ill?
    (b)   What did Louise tell him?
    (c)   Did Maugham believe her?
12 Who came to live with Louise in London?
13 What happened when Iris agreed to go out?
14 Maugham went to see Louise.
    (a)   Why did he go to see her?
    (b)   What cruel words did Maugham say to her?
    (c)   What was her reply?
15 What happened on Iris's wedding-day?
16 What were Louise's last words to her daughter?
17 How did they prove that Louise was a cruel and selfish woman?

THE ANT AND THE GRASSHOPPER

1 The story of The Ant and The Grasshopper is meant to teach
    young children a lesson. What lesson is it meant to teach?
2 Why did Maugham not like this story?
3 Why was George Ramsay looking miserable?
4 Then one day, Tom said that he did not like work.
    (a)   What did Tom do?
    (b)   What did Tom do when he needed small sums of money?
    (c)   What did Tom do when he needed large sums of money?
5 Why was George willing to help his brother?
6 What did Tom promise to do if George helped him?
7 Why did George become tired of Tom's promises?
8 Tom was going to prison . . .
    (a)   Why was Tom going to go to prison?
    (b)   How much did George pay Cronshaw?
    (c)   What did Tom and Cronshaw do with the money?
9 'A few weeks ago, Tom became engaged to an old woman.'
    (a)   How old was the woman?
    (b)   What happened to the woman?
    (c)   What happened to Tom?

10   It was the funniest story I had heard for a long time.
  (a)   Why was Maugham reminded of the story of The Ant and
        The Grasshopper?
  (b)   Why did Maugham think the story was funny?

THE FALL OF EDWARD BARNARD

1 Where did Bateman and Edward meet Isabel?
2 Why was Bateman sad that Isabel was going to marry Edward?
3 Why did Edward have to go to Tahiti?
4 How long was Edward going to be away in Tahiti?
5 Was Isabel ready to wait for him?
6 Who was Arnold Jackson?
7 Bateman spoke to Braunschmidt about Edward.
  (a)   What happened to Edward?
  (b)   What did Bateman decide to do?
8 Bateman was amazed when he heard Arnold Jackson's name. Why
   was he amazed?
9 Edward told Bateman that he had been fired from Braunschmidt's.
   Why was Bateman amazed?
10 I can't understand it, Bateman thought to himself. What could
    Bateman not understand?
11 What happened when Bateman met Arnold Jackson?
12 What did Edward say Jackson had taught him?
13 Why was Edward not staying in the best hotel?
14 Eva was beautiful.
  (a)   Who was Eva?
  (b)   Describe Eva.
15 What a strange man, Bateman thought to himself. Why did
    Bateman think Arnold Jackson was strange?
16 Why did Bateman want Edward to come back to Chicago?
17 'There are more important things in life than making money,'
    Edward said to Bateman.
  (a)   What did Edward think was more important?
  (b)   Whose happiness did Bateman say was most important?
18 Who did Edward think Isabel should marry?

19 Bateman told Isabel the whole story.
   (a)   What one question did Isabel ask?
   (b)   What did she take off her finger?
   (c)   Why had she stayed engaged to Edward?
20 Bateman could not believe what Isabel was saying. What was she
   saying?
21 As Bateman held Isabel in his arms, he had a dream.
   (a)   What was Bateman's dream?
   (b)   What did Isabel say?

W. SOMERSET MAUGHAM

unsimplified

FICTION

Liza of Lambeth
Mrs Craddock
The Magician
Of Human Bondage
The Moon and Sixpence
The Trembling of a Leaf
On a Chinese Screen
The Painted Veil
The Casuarina Tree
Ashenden
The Gentleman in the Parlour
Cakes and Ale
First Person Singular
The Narrow Corner

Ah King
Don Fernando
Cosmopolitans
Theatre
The Summing Up
Christmas Holiday
Books and You
The Mixture as Before
Up at the Villa
Strictly Personal
The Razor's Edge
Then and Now
Creatures of Circumstance
Catalina

Here and There (*Collection of Short Stories*)
Quartet (*Four Short Stories with Film Scripts*)
A Writer's Notebook
Trio (*Three Short Stories with Film Scripts*)
The Complete Short Stories (3 *Vols.*)
Encore (*Three Short Stories with Film Scripts*)
The Vagrant Mood
The Collected Plays (3 *Vols.*)
The Selected Novels (3 *Vols.*)
The Partial View
Ten Novels and Their Authors
The Travel Books

Road to Nowhere *by John Milne*

The Black Cat *by John Milne*
Don't Tell Me What To Do *by Michael Hardcastle*
The Runaways *by Victor Canning*
The Red Pony *by John Steinbeck*
The Goalkeeper's Revenge and Other Stories *by Bill Naughton*
The Stranger *by Norman Whitney*
The Promise *by R. L. Scott-Buccleuch*
The Man With No Name *by Evelyn Davies and Peter Town*
The Cleverest Person in the World *by Norman Whitney*
Claws *by John Landon*
Z for Zachariah *by Robert C. O'Brien*
Tales of Horror *by Bram Stoker*
Frankenstein *by Mary Shelley*
Silver Blaze and Other Stories *by Sir Arthur Conan Doyle*
Tales of Ten Worlds *by Arthur C. Clarke*
The Boy Who Was Afraid *by Armstrong Sperry*
Room 13 and Other Ghost Stories *by M. R. James*
The Narrow Path *by Francis Selormey*
The Woman in Black *by Susan Hill*

For further information on the full selection of
Readers at all five levels in the series, please refer
to the Heinemann Readers catalogue.

Macmillan Heinemann English Language Teaching
Between Towns Road, Oxford OX4 3PP, UK
A division of Macmillan publishers limited
Companies and representatives throughout the world

ISBN 0 435 27199 7

Heinemann is a registered trade mark of Reed Educational and ProfessionalPublishing Ltd

These stories were first published as a collection in 1951, by William
Heinemann in *W. Somerst Maugham: The Complete Short Stories*
This retold version for Heinemann Guided readers
© John Davey 1988, 1992, 2001
First published 1988
This edition published 2001

Illustrated by Paul Sullivan
Typography by Adrian Hodgkins
Cover by Janet Wooley and Threefold Design
Typeset in 11.5/14.5 pt Goudy
by Joshua Associates Ltd, Oxford
Printed and bound in Spain by Mateu Cromo, S.A.

2005 2004 2003 2002 2001
16 15 14 13 12 11 10 9 8 7